Teach Me to Be
BIG

K Monsma

Trilogy Christian Publishers
A Wholly Owned Subsidary of Trinity Broadcasting Network
2442 Michelle Drive
Tustin, CA 92780

For information, address Trilogy Christian Publishing
Rights Department, 2442 Michelle Drive, Tustin, Ca 92780.
Trilogy Christian Publishing/ TBN and colophon are trademarks of Trinity Broadcasting Network.

For information about special discounts for bulk purchases, please contact Trilogy Christian Publishing.

Manufactured in the United States of America

Trilogy Disclaimer: The views and content expressed in this book are those of the author and may not necessarily reflect the views and doctrine of Trilogy Christian Publishing or the Trinity Broadcasting Network.

10 9 8 7 6 5 4 3 2 1

Library of Congress Cataloging-in-Publication Data is available.

ISBN 978-1-64773-137-3 (Print Book)
ISBN 978-1-64773-138-0 (ebook)

"Use me, God. Show me how to take who I am, who I want to be, and what I can do, and use it for a purpose greater than myself."

"Our lives begin to end the day we become silent about things that matter."

—Martin Luther King Jr.

I'm watching you big brother
I'm studying what you do
Slow down for me just a little
So I can keep up with you

1

2

4

Show me how to love so strong
Just like you and Dad
To see the best in everyone
And to be patient when I'm mad

Teach me how to share my toys
I promise, I won't mind
Of all the things you teach me
Teach me to be KIND

8

Someday I'll be older
And I'll be on my own
So I will need to face my fears
And show you I have grown

9

Teach me how to stand up tall
To give back and behave
Of all the things you teach me
Teach me to be **BRAVE**

12

Through the years we will fight
And we will disagree
I'll need to know how to heal
And set my anger free

15

Make sure to take your time
For you are leading me
I'm going to make you proud
Just you wait and see

18

So let's find our favorite spot
Where the leaves blow in the breeze
And don't forget, most important of all
Teach me to be **BIG** please

19

CPSIA information can be obtained
at www.ICGtesting.com
Printed in the USA
LVHW011100211220
674733LV00009B/174